YOUNG ELI READERS

Jane Cadwallader

PB3
and Coco the Clown

Illustrated by Gustavo Mazali

It's night. Sally is with her uncle Coco the clown in his circus motorhome. They are having dinner. Suddenly they hear a strange noise WEEEEEEEEEEEEE!

What's that!

I don't know!

What can it be? It's round and grey.
OH! It's a SPACESHIP!

Sally and Coco run outside.
A small ET and a robot are coming down
the stairs of the spaceship.

Hello.
My name is PB3
and this is my robot,
Robin.

PB3 and Robin are very surprised.
On Planet P3 they don't have animals,
or motorhomes or even many different colours
(they only have black, grey, green and white).

Look at those funny houses!

Those aren't houses! They're elephants!

COME TO CIRCUS

Ha! Ha! This is a circus.

Coco and Sally invite PB3 and Robin to have
a cup of tea.

Do you like tea?

I don't know.

Sally is showing PB3 some photos of her family. Her father is a juggler. His name is Juggler Jim and he's very clever! Robin is taking photos of the tea.

Beautiful balls! Orange and blue and yellow and red and purple!

Tea! Brown and hot and wet!

Sally's mother, Ellie, and her aunt Mary are elephant trainers. They are both short but very strong!

These are my mum and my aunt Mary. They love elephants!

Oh! Here's another photo. It's behind the photo of Sally's mother and the elephants. It's a photo of Katya. She's an acrobat and the circus schoolteacher. She's very beautiful!

Is this another aunt?

No. It's Katya. Why is her photo here Uncle Coco?

It's time for you to go to bed Sally!

The next morning Sally goes to the circus school.
She invites PB3 and Robin to go with her.

Hello.
Welcome to the
circus school!

These are
my new friends
PB3 and Robin.

Oh! There's Coco! What's he doing on that elephant? He has some flowers for Katya. He wants to give them to her … but Katya thinks he is just practising for the show.

Coco is practising! Well done Coco!

10
×4

A+B=C

C=A+B

B=C−A

A=C−B

It's afternoon. School is finished. PB3 and Robin go to Sally's motorhome to have lunch with her mum and dad.

Goodbye Katya!

After lunch they help Coco to get dressed for the show. He wears big yellow trousers and very big black shoes, a pink and green shirt, a blue hat and a purple coat.

What a funny nose!

It's a beautiful nose!

It's my clown's nose.

It's evening and time for the show to begin. The people are going into the big top. There's Coco. He has a big red nose, a big red mouth and two very big ears! Coco is giving all the children a balloon and a big welcome.

PB3 and Robin love the circus! Coco is riding a bike. It's a very small bike! Oops! What a funny bike! It's only got one wheel! PB3 and Robin wave hello to Katya and she waves back.

Look!
There's Katya!
Hello Katya!

Come to the circus.
It's right here in town
There's Katya the acrobat
And Coco the clown.

So ... Hurray! Hurray! Hurray!
Come to the circus today
Hurray! Hurray! Hurray!
It's here in town today!

Come to the circus
Jim the juggler's great!
And you can ride on an elephant
Come now! Don't be late!

So ... Hurray! Hurray! Hurray!
Come to the circus today
Hurray! Hurray! Hurray!
It's here in town today!

4 It's time for Katya's act. Katya goes up and up and up and up! Coco pulls some flowers from his coat for Katya. He wants to give them to her … but Katya thinks it's just part of the show.

18

Katya is walking on a rope up in the Big Top.
EVERYONE is watching her.

Hm!
That's
difficult!

SUDDENLY Katya starts to fall! Everyone's surprised!

OOPS!

Be careful Katya!

PB3 hits a button on Robin's control panel and a strong wind goes round the circus. The wind is picking up all the balloons.

Hey! My balloon!

The wind carries all the balloons to the centre of the ring. Now we can't see Coco. Katya is falling down and down.

Then Katya falls into the balloons. Now we can't see Coco or Katya!

The balloons stopped Katya from being hurt. Katya and Coco come out from the balloons.

There's Katya!

There's the clown!

Thank you PB3 and Robin!

Thank you!

What a wonderful show!

▶ 5

Come to the circus.
It's right here in town
There's Katya the acrobat
And Coco the clown.

So … Hurray! Hurray! Hurray!
Come to the circus today
Hurray! Hurray! Hurray!
It's here in town today!

Come to the circus
Jim the juggler's great!
And you can ride on an elephant
Come now! Don't be late!

So … Hurray! Hurray! Hurray!
Come to the circus today
Hurray! Hurray! Hurray!
It's here in town today!

▶ 6 Karaoke music

Activity pages

1 **Put the sentences in order.**
Number the pictures.

1   circus. • They • go • to • a
2   They • Coco • meet • and • Sally.
3   falls. • Katya
4   PB3 • help. • and • Robin
5   says • Sally • thank • you.

1 | They | go | to | a | circus. |

2

3

4

5

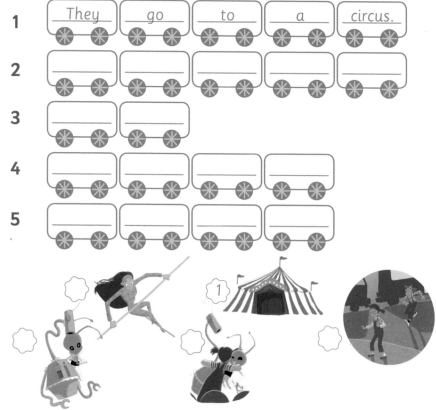

2 **Find the words. Fill the gaps in the song.**

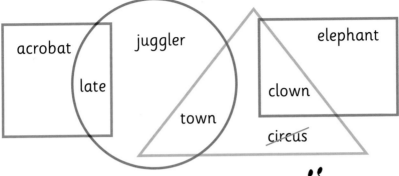

Come to the _____circus._____ (triangle)

It's right here in _____. (circle and triangle)

There's Katya the _____ (square)

And Coco the _____ (triangle and rectangle)

Come to the _____ (triangle)

Jim the _____ is great (circle)

And you can ride on an _____ (rectangle)

Come on! Don't be _____ (square and circle)

3 **Match.**

1 Robin thinks the elephants are houses.   8

2 They have a cup of tea.   14

3 They go to the circus school.   25

4 They help Coco get dressed for the show.   6

5 Katya falls into the balloons.   11

4 **Colour. Find the extra words.**
Make a sentence.

meals = orange   clothes = **purple**
family = **green**   face = yellow

shoes

aunt

mother

father

lunch

coat

mouth

Coco

Katya

dinner

uncle

nose

shirt

trousers

breakfast

loves

hat

ears

5 Write the words to make a secret code.

B E A U T I F U L   _ _ _ _ _ _ _
5 4 1 6 9 11 12 6 8   1 7 10 3 5 1 9

_ _ _ _ _   _ _ _ _ _ _ _
17 13 3 9 3   20 6 18 18 8 4 10

_ _ _ _ _ _   _ _ _ _ _
7 8 3 15 16 14   19 3 6 9 13

6 Use the secret code from activity 5
to finish the picture of Coco.

_ _ _ _   _ _   _ _ _ _ _ _
7 3 7 3   11 14   15 4 1 10 11 16 18

_   _ _ _ _   _ _ _ _ _ .
1   5 8 6 4   14 13 11 10 9

_ _   _ _ _   _ _ _ _
13 4   13 1 14   14 3 19 4

_ _ _ _ _   _ _ _ _ _ _ .
18 10 4 4 16   12 8 3 15 4 10 14

7 Decorate a circus motorhome for PB3 and Robin. Write a description.

Here is a circus motorhome for PB3 and Robin.

It _____

_____

_____

8 Do you like the story? Draw your face.

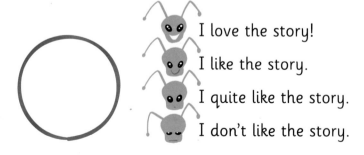

I love the story!

I like the story.

I quite like the story.

I don't like the story.